THE DE

OCTAVE MIRBEAU (1848-1917) was a prolific French journalist, novelist and playwright, who is nowadays deemed to have been a significant member of the Decadent Movement, largely because of his classic phantasmagoric fantasy *Torture Garden* (1899). Among his other novels of note are *Abbé Jules* (1888) and *The Diary of a Chambermaid* (1900).

BRIAN STABLEFORD has been publishing fiction and non-fiction for fifty years. His fiction includes an eighteen-volume series of "tales of the biotech revolution" and a series of half a dozen metaphysical fantasies set in Paris in the 1840s, featuring Edgar Poe's Auguste Dupin. His most recent non-fiction projects are *New Atlantis: A Narrative History of British Scientific Romance* (Wildside Press 2016) and *The Plurality of Imaginary Worlds: The Evolution of French* roman scientifique (Black Coat Press 2016); in association with the latter he has translated approximately a hundred and fifty volumes of texts not previously available in English, similarly issued by Black Coat Press.

OCTAVE MIRBEAU

THE DEATH OF BALZAC

TRANSLATED AND WITH AN INTRODUCTION BY
BRIAN STABLEFORD

THIS IS A SNUGGLY BOOK

ISBN: 978-1-943813-56-8

Contents

Introduction

THE triptych known as "La Mort de Balzac," by Octave Mirbeau, here translated as "The Death of Balzac," was initially written for publication in Mirbeau's *La 628-E8* (Fasquelle 1907), a book that is very difficult to classify, as it mixes an account of travels in Belgium and Holland with essays in criticism and flights of fantasy. It is generally represented as a novel, although it can equally well be regarded as a collection of shorter works hybridizing fiction and non-fiction. The three sections making up "La Mort de Balzac" were withdrawn before publication at the request of the daughter of Balzac's widow, to whom the author or publisher had presumably submitted them for comment. The protest is understandable, as Madame Hanska's treatment in the fictional part of the triptych is exceptionally nasty-minded, and the work remained unpublished during the author's lifetime. Following his death, however, it was published separately in a small edition intended for private circulation, as *Balzac* (1918), and was subsequently reintegrated into the text of *La 628-E8* in the 1939 edition. It has recently been added to the appendices of various volumes in a series of "augmented editions" of Balzac's works published as e-books by Arvensa Editions, without any indication that it is a work of fiction, thus setting a dangerous trap for unwary readers.

Octave Mirbeau (1848-1917) was a prolific journalist, novelist and playwright, who is nowadays deemed to have been a significant member of the Decadent Movement, largely because of his classic phantasmagoric fantasy *Le Jardin des supplices* (1899; tr. as *Torture Garden*). He would probably have resisted the label, as would Joris-Karl Huysmans, the other leading writer considered primarily as a Naturalist who was stuck with the Decadent label—in contrast to many of the Symbolists who were thus affiliated gladly, either by themselves or by critics and commentators. The label would also have seemed appropriate to many commentators because Mirbeau's view of life in general, and amour in particular, was extremely jaundiced, giving much of his work a cruel misanthropic—and particularly misogynistic—edge.

The fictional component of "Le Mort de Balzac" is one of his most extreme exercises in that vein, developing his thesis of the essential treachery and corruption of amour in a scathing manner.

Among his journalistic endeavors, Mirbeau contributed a large number of short stories to the feuilleton slots of newspapers in the *fin-de-siècle* period when several leading papers began using some such slots to feature short fiction rather than the serial novels that had long been their main stock-in-trade, and he honed his skill in that kind of work to near-perfection. Many of his anecdotal short stories make the customary tokenistic pretences to be "true," and there is a considerable gray area between his explicit works of fiction, and articles that represent themselves falsely as reportage. None of his other impostures of that ambiguous kind, however, are quite as brazen or as seductively persuasive in their deception as the triptych making up "La Mort de Balzac," once extracted from the context of *La 628-E8*, where its hybrid fictionality would have been more obvious, in the midst of a whole set of exercises of a similar kind.

The disguise of the triptych as documentation is aided by the fact that the first part really is an article of sorts, albeit one that plays a trifle fast and loose with matters of fact in the interests of sarcasm and satire, and the second part begins with a preparatory essay before easing into pure speculation, and finally arriving at the imagined testimony of the artist Jean Gigoux (1806-1894)—who was, of course, no longer alive in 1907 to protest the libel concocted in his name. Nor was Eveline Hanska (1805-1882), who is represented in the story with an exceptional antipathy, for which it is difficult to think of any possible reason. Mirbeau might, in his youth, have met Gigoux and Madame Hanska, but it is difficult to imagine that they could have offended him in such a way as to give rise to a grudge warranting this kind of extravagant payback.

In reality, Madame Hanska did not meet her long-time lover Gigoux until 1851, when she commissioned him to paint a portrait of her daughter, some time after the imaginary events recorded in the story. The story's breathtakingly vicious reconstruction of her character is in appallingly bad taste, but that does not detract from the fact that, seen purely as a literary exercise, the triptych is a masterpiece of sorts, in terms of the persuasiveness of its mendacious execution and the elegance of its narration. It is a gripping and affectively powerful story, artful in its very atrocity. Although not unique as a formal exercise, it is certainly very unusual, even in the context of the highly original book of which it was originally supposed to form a part, and it certainly warrants attention as a prime specimen of the work of an exceptional writer.

This translation was made from the version of the text available on-line at Wikisource.org.

Brian Stableford

THE DEATH OF BALZAC

With Balzac

I adore Balzac. Not only do I adore the epic creator of *La Comédie humaine*, but I adore the extraordinary man he was, the prodigy of humanity that he has been.

His life—what we know of it, at least—resembles his work. One can even say that it surpasses it. It was enormous and tumultuous. It was a torrent that carried everything away. Unfortunately, we know little about it. Many years of that life escape us, surely the most interesting, since they were those in which Balzac succeeded in dissimulating himself most completely. Thus, we know of a few of his liaisons that were famous. But the others? For he was a great conqueror of souls.

He was short, stout, pot-bellied and very ugly: the thickset appearance of a church cantor. The first impression he made was disagreeable. Madame Hanska said that, when she saw him for the first time, she was ashamed of her enthusiasm and only thought of fleeing. What! *That* was the sublime man, the hero?

Like all those who write a great deal, Balzac did not talk much. But when he talked, the charm took effect. There was such an authority and such a seduction in his speech that his physical disgrace was quickly forgotten. Intelligence radiated from his eyes and gave his face beauty. He was conscious of his strength of fascination, as he was conscious of his genius. It was, in any case, the same thing. Balzac created amour as he created a book. Women could not resist him any more than ideas. However, I have read the intimate and slightly ridiculous detail about him that nature had only equipped him parsimoniously for amour. He is all the more beautiful because, not having—or very scantly—the wherewithal to satisfy women, he had been given, more than any other, the delicate and rare virtue of exalting them.

Someone who had often encountered Balzac said to me: "When people talked about women he swelled with pride and strutted like a turkey . . . but he never recounted anything." In spite of his sometimes-comical infatuation, Balzac was infinitely discreet. He extended discretion regarding his sentimental life to lying, mystery and the slightly naïve complications of melodrama. He boasted of being chaste in order to conceal his vices and his good fortune. In order that no one would pick up his trail, he effaced his tracks behind him.

That discretion, so rare in a man of letters—but Balzac was not a man of letters and, fine as it is, his work is perhaps what interests us least in his regard—irritates us greatly, because it hides him from us more. He, whose European glory had popularized his features, had the power to render himself invisible when he wished. He deflected curiosities, put espionage off the track, and made use of his friends without them suspecting the role that he made them play. He had a genius for police work as he had a genius for amour, as he had a genius for everything.

One day he left—or, more exactly, he disappeared from—Paris. Absolutely nothing was known about him. Where was he? Had he shut himself away in order to work? Had he undertaken a voyage of research for his books? Was he pursuing an amorous intrigue? A financial matter? More likely an intrigue, for his research expeditions and his business trips were less mysterious. He talked about them. Almost all of them are known, including his famous voyage to Sardinia, from which he brought back the pyrites with which he dreamed of becoming a billionaire.

His absence lasted a year, or maybe two. Then one evening, without giving anyone in his entourage advance warning, he suddenly reappeared. He was seen again at the Opéra, with his blue coat and his cane, the handle of which he said—the joker—had been sculpted with gold melted down from the bracelets of his lady friends. He seemed to be resuming a conversation interrupted the previous day, was up to date with the latest salon gossip, and everything that had happened while he was not there. About his absence, not a word; he affected not to understand the allusions, albeit discreet, that were made to it.

It was claimed that there was little sincerity and a great deal of theatricality in that; that he liked play-acting for others and for himself; that he extracted a certain mystery from it, and hence importance. Perhaps so. What is certain is that there were also dramas therein.

In all that has been written about that extraordinary man, we have, so to speak, an enormous quantity of bibliographical works and literary judgments—which is not what I am looking for—but we have nothing that is really a biography.

One cannot represent as such the books by Gautier and Gozlan,[1] who recount what they saw, and surely did not see very much: exteriorities, superficial gestures and manias, with which they composed anecdotes that amuse us and which tell us nothing. Gautier and Gozlan were not friends of Balzac, who had no friends. Laurent-Jan was no better,[2] although he was the one that the master preferred. They were young disciples, fervent admirers, but intimidated, whom the great man interested a little, one might say, in his works, but not at all in his existence, and for whom respect would have closed the eyes and shut the mouth if they had seen anything abnormal or monstrous in their god.

Madame Surville has only left a few insignificant pages on her brother, a cold, banal apology from which we have not a single note to take, not

---

1 Théophile Gautier's 1859 essay on "La Vie de Balzac" is brief, but Léon Gozlan's *Balzac en pantoufles* (1856; tr. as *Balzac in Slippers*), remains a classic memoir.

2 Laurent-Jan was the pseudonym of Alphonse-Jan Laurent (1808-1877). He collaborated with Balzac on some work, and surely qualified as his friend. He was by no means the only one; Mirbeau's statement that he had none is excessive.

a single document to retain. She had, however received many confidences. When he had too full a heart, at certain excessively happy or excessively tragic moments of his life, like his first meeting, in Neuchâtel, with Madame Hanska, or the birth and the mysterious death of his last child, Balzac, in spite of his strength of self-containment, experienced the need to confide in someone. But in whom? His mother? She was a heavy burden to him, only obsessed with matters of money. His sister? In spite of the hypocritical tenderness of his dedications, he did not love her, nor did she, deep down, love him. But he was sure of her; sure that she could keep a secret, even if only for the sake of the honor of the family.

And then, she was all he had . . . And then again, doubtless childhood habit . . . She was a petty bourgeois soul, very honest, not very sensitive, who did what she could. But she could not have any comprehension of such a soul, so different from her own; she could not have any comprehension of that genius, whose visionary boldness and immortality frightened her. Moreover, Balzac did not ask her to understand him, to share his chagrins or his joys, any more than one would ask a bottle to understand why one is filling it with poison or perfume.

Madame Surville knew many things, groaned and suffered in consequence, and kept quiet.

✳

Only one man could and ought to write a life of Balzac: Monsieur de Spoelberch de Lovenjoul.[1] All that exists of documents, his inquisitive piety and his passionate curiosity has assembled. He has treasures. He guards them. And that prodigious, unique life, of which he alone knows what remain of certain attestations and authentic testimony, he has not written, and will not write. From time to time he releases meager fragments of it, he agitates poor petty images of it, as if to stimulate our curiosity, with the intention, perhaps ironic, of never satisfying it: allusions, reticences, commencements devoid of conclusions, which irritate us, and, after having excited us to the highest degree, leave us even more ignorant, more cruelly disappointed.

A dangerous game. Imagination prowls around great men, ardent, ferocious and carnivorous.

---

1 Author's note: "Written in March 1906." The note was added because the Belgian bibliophile Charles de Spoelberch de Lovenjoul (1836-1907) died before the due publication date of *La 628-E8*. His vast collection of books and manuscripts passed into the care of the Institut.

21

It is not content with idle gossip, meager bones thrown to its hunger. It is obstinate in wanting to unearth the real meat. And one day, it will "feast," but in its own fashion. One day—in order not to continue metaphors disobliging to such a noble faculty—it will invent, that being its métier, legends a thousand times more prejudicial than reality to the glory that one would have liked to preserve from the scorn of idiots, by means of silence or lies.[1]

Perhaps Monsieur de Spoelberch de Lovenjoul, who is an honorable man, a modest nature and a writer of scant strength, does not judge himself to be of sufficient stature to write a life of Balzac. I would like to reassure him. No one is expecting a work of art from him. All that is being asked of him are documents useful to the history of literature, which is very little, and to the history of humanity, which is everything. Others will do the rest.

But no. I think, in fact, that Monsieur de Spoelberch de Lovenjoul, like everyone else, or almost everyone, has a deplorable prejudice regarding great men. The great man must be a sympathetic character, as in the theater. The great man is only veritably great on condition that one remains

---

1 Including, obviously, the present text.

silent regarding his weaknesses, and diminishes all that he had of the human. Thus, Verlaine is presented to us today as a sort of worthy, routine bourgeois, like one of those excellent radical socialists, enemies of Bohemia, who pay their taxes and are the ornament of French respectability. For a great man to enter into posterity by the front door, it is necessary to dress him with thoroughly decent and base virtues, and the vulgar heroisms that enchant the crowd. He requires, like the Christian who wants to enter paradise, all the sacramental comedies, the Extreme Unction and absolution by the riff-raff of his sins.

Now, it is by virtue of his sins that a great man impassions us the most. It is by dint of his weaknesses, his absurdities, his shames, his crimes and everything that they imply of dolorous struggles, that Rousseau moves us to tears, and that we venerate him, that we cherish him, with all the respect, and all the tenderness, that is in humanity.

We ought not to submit Balzac to the rules of a vulgar anthropometry. To lock him in the narrow cell of current morality and social respect is to comprehend nothing of such a man; it is to deny, against all evidence, the prodigy and the exception that he was. We ought to accept him, love him and honor him as he was.

Everything in him was enormous, his virtues and his vices. He felt everything, desired everything and realized everything that is human. He was Blanchon, Vandenesse and Louis Lambert; he was also Rubempré; he was even Vautrin. It is necessary not to be indignant, and above all not to be astonished, if his curiosity, let us say passionate, was sometimes liberated, like nature itself, from what are called the laws of nature—which has no laws—if it went in search of sensualities or disgusts—sensations—of which we find discreet but certain traces here and there in his books, and which we could, it appears, find even more clearly in correspondence that has fallen into the hands of Monsieur Spoelberch de Lovenjoul. Would Michelangelo, Shakespeare, Goethe, kings, emperors, popes, cardinals, academicians and ignorantin friars[1] say that that was an exception? We rub shoulders every day with people whom we know to be "secret ferreters" and to whom, in accordance with their social rank, we testify no less

---

1 "Ignorantin friars" were members of the ascetic Order of Hospitaliers de Saint-Jean-de-Dieu, who adopted that nickname as a badge of humility.

esteem, amity and respect. Oscar Wilde no longer inspires anger, even in the sectarians of virtue. No one any longer has anything but dolorous pity for him and his martyrdom.

The life of Balzac? A permanent hearth of creation, a perpetual, universal desire, a frightful struggle. Fever, exaltation and hyperesthesis constituted the normal condition of his being. Thought and passions rumbled within him like active lava in a volcano. With an ease that confounds—an ease, an elementary force—he carried forward four books at a time, theater plays, newspaper polemics, business affairs of all sorts, lawsuits, voyages, building projects, debts, bric-à-brac, social relationships, an enormous correspondence and illness. Balzac wrote "Doctor Dubois trembles for my life." And in the midst of all that, one does not observe, so to speak, a collapse, a discouragement, a doubt, or a halt. He keeps going, more ardent and more precise the further he goes. The indefatigable mind sustains the overworked body, picking it up when it weakens. Far from being overwhelmed and crushed by the needs of the present, the brief hours of repose, he conceives with a marvelous lucidity the tasks of the future. Balzac did not rest on the seventh day. What an example for our paltry neurasthenics!

And he only lived for fifty-one years! Not only did he accomplish a prodigious amount of work but he dreamed and had in preparation an even more prodigious one. He left plans, perfectly worked out, for books, plays and financial affairs that three hundred years of human life would not have been sufficient to realize. When one reads the moving, stupefying *Lettres à l'Étrangère*, when one leans over the edge of that gulf, when one sees, when one hears seething, in the depths, the superhuman existence of that man, one is seized by vertigo. And one is not astonished that his brain weighed so heavily that he died of a hypertrophy of the heart.

The Académie did not want Balzac.

Monsieur Dupin[1] said to Victor Hugo: "What? Balzac, right away, in the Académie? You haven't reflected. Can that be? But there's something you haven't considered: he merits it."

---

1 The advocate André Dupin (1783-1865), all of whose publications were on legal matters; one of many Academicians widely thought to have little or no real entitlement to be there—the list in the next paragraph is not exhaustive, although the inclusion of Eugène Scribe is mischievously harsh.

He merited it; and in the eyes of Messieurs de Barante, Salvandy, Vitet, de Noailles, de Ségur, Saint-Aulaire, Lebrun, Patin, Pongerville, Villemain, Tissot, Scribe, Viennet, etc., that was, in fact, unpardonable.

But did he really merit it? How, in a way, can such a subversive, dissolute, immortal oeuvre be legitimated? How could one cover with the respectable green coat a man who was monarchist and Catholic but carried away by the power of verity beyond his own conviction, overturning so audaciously the political, economic and administrative organization of our country, displaying all social wounds, laying bare all the lies, all the violence and all the corruption of the ruling classes, and, more than any revolutionary, unleashing in souls "the horrors of the revolution"? Could that be?

Then again, Balzac had a bad reputation. He did not administer his name and his work like the good father of a family. He was not even a Bohemian—everyone knows that a Bohemian is unacademizable—he was something even worse.

The Académie admits that one can be a drunkard, a debauchee, a thief, a parricide, an atheist, and even that one might have genius, provided that one is a duke, a cardinal or very rich, and provided also that it is not known, or that only it knows; indulgent to the evil that is unknown, it is pitiless for the evil that is known. It could not be unaware that Balzac was fearfully embarrassed financially. He had undertaken disastrous enterprises; he had nearly been sunk by a resounding bankruptcy. He had debts, vile debts that he was killing himself trying to pay and of which, in the final count, he died. Like a wild boar surrounded by dogs, he went down under a pack of avid and noisy creditors. That was too lacking in elegance. Furthermore, he had no respect for propriety. Generous and ostentatious, like all those who have nothing, money did not cling to his fingers, the money of others. He bought jewelry, old historic furniture, land, town houses, country houses, and offered himself baskets of strawberries and peaches in January, which he devoured, says one chronicler of the times with "Pantagruelian gluttony." It appears that "the juice ran everywhere." Did Monsieur Viennet, an obscure, venerable and facetious poet, deliver himself to such debauches? He ate his dessert of dried figs, like everyone else . . .

"Let him pay his dues first . . . let him live modestly . . . then we'll see," said Monsieur Viennet.

Balzac did not pay his dues. He only paid in masterpieces: coin that was not legal tender in the Académie.

His financial affairs? They have been mocked a great deal, and still are. Naivety, perhaps, or indelicacy, who knows? In any case, ignorance and enchantment. That was the weak point, the crack, in that robust organism. Anyway, how can anything serious be expected of someone who writes novels?

Monsieur de Rothschild, whom he saw frequently, and of whom such a surprising and unforgettable portrait remains to us, in his Nucingen, was amused by him as if by a good farce. The most indulgent of his admirers plead that Balzac was a great constructor of chimeras—to put it more prosaically, a madman. Others caption that image with the word *fantasist*.

Men of finance are generally very limited, and arrogant with mediocrity. They lack culture, imagination and generosity of spirit, in a métier that requires a great deal. They have nothing but routine in an adventure that requires none at all. To conceive an affair is to conceive a poem. The businessman who is not, at the same time, an idealist and a poet, is nothing . . . nothing, most of the time, but a crook.

Balzac was a poet. He had a passion for beautiful and great dispositions. He did not follow ideas, he was in advance of them. In the same way that a phrase was sufficient for him to reconstitute, in his logical verity, an entire human being, a fact, sometimes a meager fact, was sufficient for him to discover and create at a stroke the drama of a business affair. He conceived it, planned it and built it with the same powerful imagination, the same faculty of divination, the same frank neatness, as his books. He would have astonished and caused to reflect men less prejudiced and less theoretically based than financiers, with the abundance and the accuracy of his technical learning, knowledge and often prescience, of the geological and economic value of the various countries of Europe. His affairs were doubtless chimerical, above all because they always came too soon. If one wants immediate glory or money it is always necessary to come later . . . after someone else. Genius sows and passes on. Skill remains, waits and harvests. Balzac sowed; often, the seed was good. Many of his affairs at which people laughed were realized subsequently by others: a familiar epilogue.

The work, which is a work of bitter psychology and, in spite of its worship of money, a work of critical social pessimism, is at the same time a work of universal divination. Solidly established on the contemporary, it engages with and predicts the future. Balzac is as much at ease in tomorrow as he is in today. His financial conceptions would do honor to a revolutionary economist. He glimpses new directions in the movement of State funds, bold solutions to agricultural problems. He sketches practical, ingenious plans for societies of mutual aid, like, for example, the Societé des Gens de lettres, which emerged from his brain. (It seems, moreover, to have forgotten him, for it refused his effigy from the genius of Auguste Rodin, just as the Académie had refused his person from the genius of Victor Hugo.)

He dreamed and prepared an entire revolution of bookselling by the creation of the cheap book. His sense of life, of the orientation of life, enabled him to discover, before everyone else, the speculative value of land in certain quarters of Paris, then deserts, which have now become centers of activity and wealth. He rejoiced in having bought a plot of land in Sèvres. More than fifteen years before the establishment of railways in France he wrote: "One day, we shall have a railway between

Paris and Brest, and a station will be constructed very close to my house. Do as I do, buy, buy." His house was at Les Jardies. The station is there. But what he had not foreseen is that, later, at Les Jardies, Messieurs Rouvier, Étienne, Thomson and Joseph Reinach would celebrate a cult, but that the cult would not be that of Balzac, but that of Gambetta.[1]

Moralists have tried to prove that Balzac invented, all of a piece, mores, social compartments, an entire artificial world—the world of Balzac, as they call it, by contrast with the world of reality—and that an entire category of ambitious individuals, sharpers and adventurers, seduced by brilliant vices and triumphant immortality of his work, have, in a sense, molded their souls on those of his imaginary heroes. That is stupidity. He did not invent them; he foresaw them, as he also foresaw Wagner and Wagnerism, and as he had glimpsed, in spite of his confused notions of art, the heights where the name of Auguste Rodin is today resplendent.

I have been told that one day, while chatting with his friends, Balzac imagined, laughing—was

---

1 The Republican politician Léon Gambetta took up residence in 1878 in the Maison des Jardies in Sèvres, where Balzac had lived between 1838 and 1840.

he laughing as much as they wanted to believe?—a reliable and rapid means of making a lot of money, enough money to found a great newspaper, a newspaper of influence and interests and, the idea of which had often haunted him.

"Nothing is simpler," he explained, "and within the scope of all intelligences. It's a matter of publishing a little weekly newssheet, which would be called the *Physicians' Journal*. The sheet would contain nothing except the list of that week's deaths, with the name of the physician in regard to each death. It would be distributed in the streets, like a prospectus. You can see the physicians from here . . . it would be enormous."

And Balzac laughed uproariously at that invention.

Now, a few years later, an American, at the end of his resources, who was absolutely unaware of that sally on Balzac's part, realized that idea of Balzac's. It was the point of departure of one of the largest fortunes and one of the greatest newspapers in the world.

The nastiest rumors circulated about Balzac, hawked and exaggerated by his enemies. Not only was he Rubempré and Vautrin; he was also

Mercadet. Publishers, printers and newspaper editors complained loudly about his bad faith, and his scabrous capability. Those poor fellows wept over having been "rooked" by him with the most astonishing mastery. They accused him of indelicacy because, knowing like an advocate all the complications of legal procedure, he defended himself, often victoriously, against their rapacity. Was it not also said that he lived off his mistresses? Was it not affirmed that he had borrowed, in a fashion skirting the criminal, a large sum of money from Madame D***, a printer's wife who adored him? Was it not said, finally, that before his marriage he obtained nearly two hundred thousand francs from Madame Hanska?

There is some truth in all these domestic stories, but a poorly understood truth, a deformed truth, as usual. He did not hide it. The *Lettres à l'Étrangère*, which, in spite of the fine cries of amour, the fine cries of pride, the exaltations to have confidence in him, the overflow of a personality drunk on itself, and in spite of that enormous conceit that made him puff himself up to the point of buffoonery, are the most moving, the most anguishing martyrology that one can imagine of the life of an artist, contain confessions— veiled, it is true—and histories, doubtless obscure but recognizable for anyone who knows a little about Balzac's secret existence. There is often mention of a "sacred debt." Might that not be an allusion to the debt to Madame D***?

We can believe anything of a man whose life was money, money everywhere and always money. "Money," writes Taine,[1] "was the persecutor and the tyrant of his life. He was its prey and its slave, by virtue of need, honor, imagination and hope. That dominator and executioner bent him over his labor, chained him there, inspired him, pursued him in his leisure, in his reflections, in his dreams, mastered his hand, forged his poetry, animated his characters and spread the stream of its splendors over his entire oeuvre." The stream of its dolors too, and its shames.

Let us go back for a moment to those letters, in which the author of *La Comédie humaine* evokes a tremendous Inferno of labor and money; let us recall the terrible necessities, the terrible reckonings that the end of every month brought, the bailiff on his heels, his mother harassing him, the future engaged, the pangs of his liver and the choking of his heart; the novel that he had to deliver the next day; his nights, after emerging from a social din-

---

1 Hippolyte Taine published his essay "Balzac: A Critical Study" in the *Journal des Débats* in 1858; it was reprinted many times thereafter.

ner or an evening at the Opéra, spent in writing, writing, writing! With regard to *Modeste Mignon*, he announced joyfully to his friend: "Another seventy pages of my writing . . . it will be finished tomorrow." In that labor of a convict, which would have been, for anyone else, an exhausting delirium, he did not lose his footing for a single minute. He conserved, intact, the mastery of his brain.

He thinks of everything, even the smallest things. He sketches malicious portraits, recounts witty anecdotes jovially about Princesse Belgiojoso, Madame de Girardin or Comtesse Potocka. He promises to go, the next day, to the jeweler, to see where the ring is that he ordered for his dear Constance Victoire, for which he has provided the design. He takes charge of the purchase of her gloves and a thousand little trinkets. With the clarity, the practical and shrewd sense of a businessman and a man of law, he submits to his Line a complete plan for the reorganization of her fortune; he explains, with the competence of an agronomist, what new profit she can obtain from her uncultivated lands, indicates to her, with the clairvoyance of a banker, a more judicious placement of her money. He guides her in her lawsuit, in her claims, in the confused and difficult situation in which the death of her husband has left her, and that is in a country whose mores and judicial procedures he scarcely knows.

Recall, too, the obstinate hopes, the grandiose dreams of the future harvest, very imminent, the almost savage confidence he has in his genius. And see him draw up, with perfect honesty, the balance sheet of today's debts and tomorrow's assured triumphs. What are his debts? Nothing. What do his debts weigh? Nothing, in truth, nothing at all! Does he not have his oeuvre, growing larger every day, more popular every day, which reserves millions for him? Does he not have his business affairs, which represent billions? So he takes, as he can, where he can, small advances on that certain fortune, advances that he will reimburse later, tomorrow, this evening, perhaps a hundredfold.

And the chimeras accumulate, rising up from everywhere, enveloping him with their caresses and singing round him. Their voices lull him and reanimate him. He forgets his distress therein; he even forgets the frightful pains that are quartering the bones in his breast. She and he, she, Line, Linette, the dear Minou, he, the good, the great, the sublime Noré, will finally attain the happiness so long awaited. They will have a palace, like kings, will live in a marvelous décor of art, feasts, domination; they will live in Paris, with the world at their feet. Is it for a few miserable hundreds of thousands of francs that it is necessary to slow down, to halt the flight of his genius, to renounce his magnificent creations, to steal from the amour that exalts him, to steal from the world that he dazzles, a glory with which he feels himself replete, but to which it is necessary to give money to eat, more money, and money forever?

Balzac's Wife

AND here I am at the best, and also the least-known, drama of Balzac's life, his marriage. Although certain episodes are still obscured from us of that extraordinary story of amour, and simultaneously the scorn, of two excessively literary hearts, the final fall of two similarly disappointed ambitions, I can perhaps add a few enlightenments to it. I hasten to say to whom I owe them: the painter Jean Gigoux, who was mingled very intimately, as intimately as Balzac, with the life of Madame Hanska. To authenticate certain grave facts, one of which, at least, is of the greatest tragic horror, I have, it is true, only spoken confidences. But why should spoken confidences be considered any less true than written confidences? They have, on the contrary, every chance of being more so. Jean Gigoux was very old when he made them to me, and very disillusioned; he no longer had any pride. I have always thought that it required great courage, or great cynicism—which is often the same thing—for him to get to the end of his confidence.

Everyone knows how Balzac made the acquaintance of Madame Hanska. In sum, it is the most banal story: a letter of enthusiastic admiration, found by him at the offices of his publisher, Léon Gosselin, on 28 February 1832. It came from the depths of Russia and was signed *L'Étrangère*. Balzac was very vain; he had all the great aspects, so to speak, of vanity, and all the petty ones as well. That letter delighted him, exalted his self-esteem as a man and as a writer immensely.

Unfortunately, we do not have that letter. It is supposed the Balzac burned it, along with many others of the same origin, after a violent drama that occurred in 1847, it is believed, between Madame Hanska and himself. What we know about that letter is from Balzac himself, who told Madame Surville and a few friends that it was admirable, that it revealed "an extraordinary woman." It was in vain that he strove to discover the author. Seven months later, he received another . . .

That one, we have. It is very romantic, very emphatic and very stupid, and it already slides, unfortunately, from literature into amour.

Within it is written, word for word, this:

"You must love and be loved: the union of angels must be your lot, your souls must have unknown felicities; l'Étrangère loves you both and wants to be your friend. She too knows how to love; but that is all. Oh, you will understand me!

And further on:

"Your career is brilliant, strewn with sweet flowers and embalmed."

He was offered, this time, a slightly mysterious means of correspondence. Many people would have thrown those letters in the waste-paper basket, for I suppose that in those days, literary correspondents, like those of today, were, as often as not, hysterical or imploring old women. Balzac conserved the letters piously, and replied to them.

In the course of that correspondence, he learned, not without an intoxicated joy, that l'Étrangère was a great lady. Naturally, she was young, beautiful, a countess, "colossally rich," married to a man who did not love her, and superior in intelligence and heart to all other women. His mind, so alert, so sharp, so profoundly human, believed, with a theological fervor, in great ladies. Like Paul Bourget, for whom that common trait was sufficient for him to devote a passionate admiration to Balzac, and to believe himself to be a Balzac, he delighted in titles and blazons. Immediately, he fell in love, recklessly, with the unknown great lady. Immediately, to conquer her esteem, to stir her sensibility, he displayed before her his difficult life, confided to her his projects, his dreams, his rancors, his incessant struggles, the long martyrdom of his genius. With the aid of his imagination, he built, on the distant fragility of that amour, the most marvelous of his novels, and perhaps, already, the most solid of his business affairs.

Barbey d'Aurevilly, who always liked to talk about Balzac and anything related to Balzac, made me this portrait of Madame Hanska. She had an imposing and noble beauty, a trifle massive, a trifle stout; but she was able to conserve in her plumpness a very lively charm, spiced by a delightful foreign accent and "very impressive" sensual allures. She had admirable shoulders, the most beautiful arms in the world, a complexion of radiant splendor. Her exceedingly dark eyes, slightly troubled and disquieting; her mouth, thick and very red; her heavy hair, framing a forehead of infinitely pure design with English curls; and the serpentine smoothness of her movements, gave her an air of simultaneous abandonment and dignity, a haughty and lascivious expression whose savor was rare and gripping. Very intelligent, with an extensive but slightly confused culture, she liked to interest herself in conversation in the highest questions, which revealed the abundance of her reading far more than the originality of her ideas. She was neither witty not cheerful and manifested in all things a great exaltation of sentiments. In truth, she was a trifle disequilibrated, without a clear idea of what she wanted.

"In sum," d'Aurevilly said to me, "she was worth the trouble of all follies."

He had only known her after Balzac's death, and not for long. He confessed to me that the continual presence of Jean Gigoux in the house in the Rue Fortunée, his vulgarity as a male conqueror of women, his cynicism in sprawling on Balzac's furniture, his art-student affectation of "spitting on the rugs" quickly made him intolerable and odious. Not long after being introduced to Madame de Balzac, d'Aurevilly no longer went to her house. But until the end of his life he had conserved a deep impression of that glimpsed face.

We scarcely know Madame Hanska except through Balzac's letters—for I want to neglect for the moment the indications that came to me from Jean Gigoux, which might appear suspect and of a very limited psychology. And again, we cannot always trust Balzac, who often lies, like all amorous individuals. His foolish vanity leads him, unwittingly, to the least acceptable exaggerations. He has a mania for never showing us Madame Hanska except via himself. And then, has it not been claimed that *Lettres à l'Étrangère* are, in places, a very untrustworthy document? Has it not been affirmed that Madame Hanska, after Balzac's death, wrote or rewrote the amorous parts? I do not know whether there is any truth in that accusation. It appears to me, personally, very risky. The reasons given for it have not convinced me, for everything holds together in those letters. They form such a beautiful uniform sequence, they are marked with such a personal imprint, that one cannot admit the possibility of an ulterior revision. In any case, we are reduced, with regard to that figure and its true character, to poorly confirmed references and worse, simple hypotheses. Although she is so close to us, a veil hides her from us that will not soon be lifted.

One can reconstitute Madame Hanska's state of mind when she resolved to write her first letter to Balzac. Relegated to the depths of the Ukraine, with a husband much older than her, unsociable and solely preoccupied with material interests, she was bored. Alone, or almost alone, in that sort of exile, in the middle of a puerile and barbaric land, she could not find anything to occupy her ardent imagination and her passionate heart. She was a misunderstood and sacrificed wife. For want of sentimental action, she read a great deal and dreamed even more. And through reading and dreaming, she felt very unhappy.

French writers, who are those who know the most and speak the best about amour, attracted her particularly, and above all the others, Balzac, whose genius she had understood immediately, and whose celebrity, with all that it then contained of the slightly scandalous, inflamed her. She became vividly smitten with that Parisian existence, voluptuous, adventurous and excessive, which he depicted with such dazzling colors. She became ecstatic before those figures of women with hearts of fire, hearts of tears, or hearts of poison, in which she found, in full action, in settings of such feverish warmth, all her dreams and the furious impetus of life, of all life, which incessantly broke against the walls of that silent and cold old manor, with the dead faces and dead surfaces of its muzjiks and its ponds.

So, what initially impelled her toward Balzac was her sentimental idleness, her astonished gratitude for a man who specified and summarized so well all the intimate intoxications and all the secret desires of woman. It was also something more vulgar, it is permissible to suppose: a bluestocking instinct that hoped to profit from the illustriousness of a great poet, by engaging with him in a correspondence that posterity might one day collect. The case is not rare, and it is almost always unfortunate. What can we expect of the moving, the elegant and the natural from someone who poses before such an objective?

However, there is no doubt that Madame Hanska and Balzac loved one another passionately, and that their love surpassed, at least in the beginning, the piquant attraction of a mysterious correspondence, calculations of interest and the schemes of a mutual ambition. All that only came later.

How could they not have loved one another? To maintain and exalt their amour they had two powerful tonics, two admirable stimulants: imagination and distance. Between 1833, the date of their first meeting in Neuchâtel, and 1848, the date of Balzac's last voyage to Russia, they only saw one another four times. Four times in fifteen years!—three times at Wierzchownia, and once in Paris, where Madame Hanska came with her daughter, after the death of her husband, for a brief sojourn. For individuals who live primarily via the brain, what better means is there than absence to eternalize a sentiment that does not ordinarily resist the quotidian disenchantments of presence and the brutalities of contact?

During those visits, disillusionment did not come, could not come. Balzac does not want to compromise anything and he is under arms. He watches himself; he masters himself. He puts a brake on the overflow of his personality; he softens the roughness of his character and his manias. He becomes coaxing, feline, very tender, a child. He is charming and submissive. And he is unhappy too, for, more than admiration and tenderness, he requires pity. He is misunderstood, he is calumniated, he is persecuted—him, who has only grandeur, sublimity and genius! He is able to be cheerful on occasion, melancholy when it is necessary to be, at the hour of the Russian dusk, so penetrating and so profound! With his customary skill, by means of beautiful cries, he is able to exploit all the tenderness of an infatuated and conquered soul. Even in their moments of exaltation, they never let go of themselves, and they always lie to one another. Is that not perfect amour?

When Balzac leaves, when they separate—for how long, alas!—they have not known a single minute of lassitude, or disappointment. On the contrary. Absence is going to give more youth, more strength to the passion. Both of them, in the heroic expectation of seeing one another again, go to make a new provision of joys, chimeras and hopes. And the letters recommence, more urgent and more ardent, with slight quarrels here and there, little coquetries, not serious and not dolorous, which only feed their adoration further. After that rest, that pause, Balzac resumes, more intrepidly than ever, his rosary of misery, his breathless life, his terrible convict labor . . . and his mistresses. Is it not marvelous to think that that grand amour did no harm at all to his other amours? In the same way that he could write four books at once, he could love four women at the same time. He was rich enough in imagination to love them all.

We can specify the day, and even the moment, when the idea of marrying Madame Hanska took hold of Balzac's mind resolutely. Such as you know him, you will not be astonished that the idea came to him as soon as he had been informed, albeit very vaguely, of l'Étrangère's situation, and what he might be able to get out of it.

There was, of course, a husband; but the husband did not embarrass him. He suppressed him at a stroke, straight away. He crossed the husband out, like a typographical error.

In a letter in which he told his sister, Madame Surville, with boyish enthusiasm, about the meeting in Neuchâtel, he wrote: "And I won't talk about the colossal wealth. What is that compared with such a masterpiece of beauty?" He comes back to it, however, a few lines lower down . . . and then, further on: "As for our husband, as he's heading toward sixty, I've sworn to wait, and she to reserve her hand and heart for me . . ." Two months later, in Geneva where he had followed the couple, and where he stayed for five weeks, the marriage is entirely decided. After that, they mention it often in their letters. There are allusions on every page to that settlement, incessantly put off; there are detailed plans for a union that seems, in fact, to have been desired much more by Balzac than Madame Hanska.

Naturally, it is necessary to wait for the good Monsieur Hanski to disappear. His state of health permits the supposition, moreover, that they will not have to wait for long. Monsieur Hanski, informed, does not put up any opposition to those posthumous projects. It is even claimed that he approves of them, if not that he encourages them. In spite of his difficult character and his unliterary aspirations, that accommodating Cossack is on the best of terms with Balzac, and honored to be his friend. Balzac has conquered him too, perhaps by way of his agronomic science. Monsieur de Spoelberch de Lovenjoul possesses, and has published, a letter in which the gentleman expresses his esteem and admiration to the author of *La Comédie humaine*. Although Balzac is of very scant nobility, the other is rather flattered to know that such a person will one day replace him, if not in the heart of his wife, which he has never possessed, at least in her bed. There is a comical underside to that entire history, of which, unfortunately, we know very little.

Thus it is that at Neuchâtel, on the day of the meeting, Madame Hanska is sitting, as has been agreed, on a bench on the promenade, with her husband and her children. In order to be recognized she has to hold on her knees a novel by Balzac, clearly in evidence. The book is there but the emotion of the poor woman is such that she does not perceive that it is completely hidden by a scarf. A little man, fat and very ugly, goes past, and then comes back.

Oh my God, Madame Hanska says to herself, *as long as it's not him!*

She finally notices her mistake. She uncovers the book. The man immediately approaches. Very pale, she says, in a cry of despair: "It's him! It's him!"

And a few moments later, "in the shade of a great oak," while Monsieur Hanski has gone who knows where, they exchange the first kiss and the promise of engagement!

Naturally, too, they will wait until Balzac has paid his debts, and reestablished his affairs. A matter of a few months, of course! But what snags, what successive disillusionments . . . they go from bad to worse, his affairs . . . In spite of the optimistic calculations, the miraculous figures with which Balzac tries to decoy himself, over and over again, debts are added to debts, difficulties accumulate on top of difficulties: every day, a new obstacle.

But he does not let go of his hopes; not for a second does his confidence abandon him. In view of the marriage, always imminent, in order to ornament his house, which he wants to be sumptuous and regal, he has bought, on credit more often than not, marvelous furniture, paintings by old Italian masters, precious carpets, which he subsequently sells at a loss, pressed as he always is by an immediate need for money.

From his study in Paris he supervises and directs Madame Hanska's interests, as anxious about the returns of her fortune as if it were his own. What dreams of splendor! What schemes of genius! What affairs he must have built on that wealth and the brilliance of the foreign name that he will soon impose on the admiration of Paris!

For her part, Madame Hanska dreams of a new, enlarged life. Her eyes are always turned toward Paris, where her friend is living and working, struggling, suffering and waiting; toward Paris, where her beauty, her intellectual superiority, her romantic adventure and the great name of Balzac will assure her an exceptionally privileged, resounding position . . .

The bleak existence that she leads out there weighs upon her more and more. She needs action and expansion, intoxicated by the promise of the feminine royalty that Balzac agitates incessantly before her. And her mirror tells her every day that she is a little bit older, that her beauty is withering here, and is running to fat there. It is high time . . .

Intelligent as she is, Paris, in the depths of its distant lands, appears to her, as it does to ambitious petty individuals in the provinces, to be the unique city, the magical city, from which one can draw anything with full hands: pleasures, triumphs and domination. For that was the romantic era when all desires climbed the Butte Montmartre and, on seeing the city extended beneath them, cried: "And now, Paris, it's just the two of us!"

To hasten the moment of deliverance and conquest, she aids Balzac with her purse. But that aid, like all the others, falls in vain into a bottomless pit.

It seems, however, without the profound cause being clearly visible, that there were often, at all times, even in the times of the initial happiness, sudden pauses in the impetus of those surges, and hesitations, if not tears, which sometimes traversed in an anxious flight, the beautiful dreams of that promised life.

Shortly before February 1848, Balzac, deceiving his creditors, had succeeded in putting a large sum in shelter from their demands, still in view of his marriage. That sum, on the advice of Baron de Rothschild, he had converted into shares in the Northern Railway. But fatality is pursuing him. The Revolution arrives, which sweeps everything away. Prices on the Bourse fall to negligibility.

He is ruined. That was a terrible moment, which nearly defeated him. But, picking up the debris of that fortune, borrowing here, borrowing there, further pledging a future already pledged in all directions, he no longer hesitates; he departs for Russia. He understands clearly, this time, that it is all over, that he is doomed, that the only resource remaining to him is to marry. Whatever the cost, it is necessary to return to Paris with a wife—which is to say, with a fortune.

One can put a figure on the illusion toward which he was going. Encountering Victor Hugo on the eve of his departure, he said to him: "Yes, I'm going to Russia . . . a business matter . . . I'll bring back ten millions."

During the twenty months that that absence lasted, what happened between Madame Hanska and him? No one really knows—or rather, we are completely ignorant. I believe that Monsieur de Spoelberch de Lovenjoul does not possess any document of that period. Even Jean Gigoux only talked to me about it in vague terms. His memories were very confused, he said. It seems, in fact, that during his intimacy with Madame Hanska, Gigoux was never much preoccupied with things of the past, and that he had limited his curiosities, almost uniquely picturesque or gallant, to the events of the present, and only to those in which he had his part in the action.

He believed, however, that he had heard Madame Hanska say that Balzac had had great difficulty persuading her. She had reflected, and wanted to renounce a union that had been subject to so many hitches, and which no longer tempted her. It appears, too, that Balzac had changed enormously. He lost his seduction and his gentility, manifesting a despotic authority and bizarre manias that frightened her. His mask having fallen, he became rude and violent. And then too, he was very ill. Out there, he had crises of the liver and the heart. Mental decadence and physiological destruction were commencing. Finally, Madame Hanska's entourage tried to put her off the marriage. It was even claimed that the Emperor had put his veto on it. Oh, the poor woman had retreated a long way from all her dreams!

It is necessary to believe that Balzac's tenacious eloquence, or perhaps Madame Hanska's pity, had been stronger than anything. I remember that when I emitted the hypothesis of pity, Gigoux raised his arms toward the ceiling and said, with an ironic smile:

"Madame Hanska's pity? Oh, my dear . . . !"

Personally, I know nothing. But I know that there are things that Jean Gigoux could not understand.

What is certain is that, one evening in the month of May 1850, Balzac returned to Paris, married—married, and almost dying.

Monsieur de Spoelberch de Lovenjoul recounts[1] that on that evening, Balzac and his wife descended from a carriage, very tired, worn out by the journey, in front of number 12 Avenue Fortunée. He had written his mother a very long and detailed letter from Russia in which he had announced the date and time of her return and recommended her to put everything in the house in order and in celebration. He wanted everything to be cheerful and smiling to welcome them, with the furniture and ornaments in their place . . . light and flowers everywhere . . . a supper nicely prepared. He begged her above all to go home, because he only wanted to introduce her daughter-in-law to her the following day, solemnly. He attached a great deal of importance to those forms of protocol.

---

1 This reference is false; having been in the realm of pure speculation for some time, from now on we are in the realm of pure fantasy.

Madame de Balzac carried out her son's orders scrupulously. Her mission terminated she went home, leaving the house decorated, the flowers and the supper in the charge of a domestic whom she had engaged personally for the occasion, and whose name was François Munck.

They arrive. They see the house fully illuminated. They ring. No one responds. They ring again. Nothing. All the windows are illuminated. A large lamp is shining over the steps of the perron. But nothing stirs. Everything is still and silent, more frightening than if it were all dark. What is happening, then? Balzac is afraid. He calls out, and hammers on the gate. Still nothing. A few passers-by gather, thinking that there has been an accident of a crime, and offer their aid. They unite their efforts, their fists, their cries . . . in vain. In the meantime, the coachman has unloaded the baggage on to the sidewalk. The night is fresh. Madame de Balzac is cold. She pulls the flaps of her cloak more tightly about her and walks back and forth, stamping her feet on the pavement. She becomes impatient. Balzac becomes agitated. Going from one to another, he explains to the passers-by.

"It's incredible . . . I'm Monsieur de Balzac . . .

this is my house. I'm returning from a voyage. We're expected. Oh, I don't understand it at all!"

Someone proposes going to look for a locksmith. He knows one in a neighboring street. His name is Marminia. He is a good locksmith . . .

"So be it," Balzac consents, who nevertheless finds that means of entering his own home a trifle humiliating. "A locksmith . . . that's it . . ." For, after all, Monsieur de Balzac cannot remain in the street at such an hour of the night.

While waiting for the locksmith, they are still knocking at the door; they try throwing little pebbles at the window, and shouting: "Hey, open up! It's us! I'm Monsieur de Balzac!"

Uselessly.

Other passers-by arrive. Madame de Balzac is sitting on a trunk, very weary, her head in her hands. Balzac goes back and forth, still explaining:

"I'm Monsieur de Balzac . . . I would never have believed . . . It's extraordinary!

Finally, the locksmith is brought, who breaks through the grille. Followed by his nocturnal friends, who intend to protect him from who knows what, Balzac traverses the little courtyard very rapidly, and goes into the house. There, the most surprising spectacle is offered to his eyes.

The valet de chambre François Munck has suddenly gone mad. He has devastated the supper, scattering and breaking the crockery. The furniture is dancing in the rooms; flowers are strewn on the parquet everywhere. A broken bottle is finishing spreading a frothy liquid over the carpet, and the unfortunate fellow is delivering himself to a thousand extravagances. They take possession of him, hold him tight and lock him in a little room. He allows himself to be taken without overmuch trouble, laughing more than defending himself. Calm being restored, Balzac thanks his valiant friends, apologizes, shows them out, has the luggage brought in from the courtyard and goes to bed. He is stifling. He has a fever. Collapsed in a corner of the bedroom, increasingly enervated, Madame de Balzac does not even think of taking off her traveling cloak, and weeps "all the tears in her body."

That little drama impressed her deeply. She saw the most ominous presages therein.

Alas, a more dolorous reality, which they had not dared to admit as yet, had preceded those presages of misfortune. That was no longer a presage, it was the brutal, inexorable fact of a definite situation.

They had come back married, and enemies.

Of all that grand amour, which fifteen years of absence had exalted, a few months of communal life had sufficed to ensure that nothing remained . . . nothing but disappointment, rancor and hatred. One might say that their veritable separation dated from that moment, when they entered the house riveted together.

Of the intimate tragic scenes and the domestic quarrels that followed that lamentable arrival at the hearth, we know absolutely nothing. They must have been violent and shameful. But not one document of them survives. If any ever existed, they disappeared in the severe triage that Madame de Balzac made of the great man's papers after his death. Three years before, Balzac had burned all Madame Hanska's letters—doubtless the impulsive act of a lover. Now it was for Madame Hanska to destroy Balzac's letters—perhaps an act of reflective prudence. Will her memory benefit from that regrettable absence of information? Will it, on the contrary, be aggravated? I cannot judge.

I can only refer to the memories of Jean Gigoux. They are precise, and they have the value of witness evidence. What I find there is that Balzac and his wife did not forgive one another for having deceived one another mutually. Balzac now knew that his wife was not as rich as he had believed. From the liquidation of her affairs and her lawsuits, she had, in sum, saved very little, almost nothing. Almost nothing for Balzac. And the marriage to which he had, so to speak, clung ferociously, as to his last resource, the marriage that he had thought was his salvation, the end of his embarrassments, the apotheosis of his life, was only, in the end, one more embarrassment and one burden more. Still beautiful, doubtless, and remarkably endowed with intelligence? But what is that before such a collapse of his hopes? It was neither beauty nor intelligence of which he had gone in search out there, in the depths of the savage Ukraine. It was the money, always the money. And there was no more money; at least, no longer enough money. So, everything had to recommence.

And her? This, therefore, was the conclusion of all the promises of social triumph, literary glory and an adulated, intoxicated life, all the dreams of universal domination by which, for fifteen years, she had been numbed, lured, stolen and finally enchained to a cadaver! They ended in this house guarded by a madman, this disparate and disorderly house, like the very existence of its owner, this house that cried hatred, the fever of the life of a prostitute or a Bohemian, precarious luxury, the lurches of day-to-day existence, this house with its rooms, here full of a sometimes dubious and fake bric-à-brac, there empty and desolate, where there were outlines in chalk on the walls in the places of items of furniture sold or sent for sale. They ended with that man, ridiculously ugly, isolated from everyone and everything, tracked by all sorts of creditors, devoid of friends, devoid of family ties, ruined financially, ruined in health, whose gross flesh already reeked of putrescence and death!

With what bitterness she must have reproached herself for that phrase in her first letter—"The union of angels must be your lot!"—which had been the point of departure of all this misfortune!

They had duped one another, each duped by the other, having believed sincerely that one can transform into spiritual impulses and amorous exaltations that which is most vulgar and precise in human desire. And fifteen years . . . fifteen years of projects, dreams, mad ideas and lies, only to observe, in one day, that double scorn and that double fall!

From then on, it was finished.

A week after their arrival in Paris, overwhelmed by reproaches, fatigued by disgust, they resolved to live apart in the house, knowing that they could put more distance between one bedroom and another than there was between Paris and Wierzchwnia. And they did not meet up again, even at meals.

In any case, Balzac was almost always in bed. A circle of iron tightened increasingly around his breast. He spent his nights suffocating, seeking in vain, at the open window, to seize a little of the air that could no longer dilate his lungs. His legs swelled up and sweated; the edema reached the abdomen, the thorax. He did not complain; he did not despair. Confidently, as he had waited for the fortune, he waited for the cure, in order to get back to work, with a youth, an energy, an immense need to create, which sustained him until the death-throes. In the midst of the putrefaction of his organs, his brain remained healthy and intact. Imagination reigned there as an immaculate sovereign. He never ceased to form projects and more projects, plans for books, plans for comedies, accumulating material for the work to come. He had lost none of his marvelous fecundity.

Every day, he asked his doctor, the faithful Nacquart: "Do you think that I'll be able to resume work tomorrow? Hurry up! It's necessary . . . it's necessary . . ."

Madame de Balzac, anxious, nervous, not knowing which way to turn, ran around the city. She had discovered Polish relatives, Russian friends. One day, in one of the salons that she frequented, she encountered the painter Jean Gigoux, who offered to paint her portrait. He was very handsome; he had hard muscles, a noisy joy, and the long moustaches of a Gaulish warrior. She gave herself to him, passionately, furiously.

Balzac's Death

I shall leave Jean Gigoux the care of recounting Balzac's death, on the terrible day of 18 August 1850. That story is here, such as I had it from him, such as I wrote it down the same evening when I went home. I have not changed anything. I have not embroidered it, nor supplemented it, nor attenuated it.

It was in his studio, among all the beautiful things and all the beautiful works that he had collected. He said to me:

"Victor Hugo has recounted Balzac's death in *Choses vues*. Those pages are extremely beautiful and poignant. I don't know of anything more powerfully tragic, but they are somewhat inexact, in that they do not show sufficiently the abandonment in which the great writer died. Perhaps Hugo, who admired and liked Balzac a great deal, recoiled before the horror of the truth. The real truth is that Balzac died abandoned by everyone and everything, like a dog."

At the word "dog" a large russet spaniel that was sleeping curled up on the carpet twitched its tail and turned its head toward its master.

"No, no," said the latter, who leaned over to stroke the animal's silky fur, "Be tranquil, my boy. You won't die like Balzac! Someone will close your eyes!"

And he went on:

"Hugo claims to have been received in the house by Madame Surville. He claims that he conversed for a few minutes with Monsieur Surville, that he had seen Madame de Balzac at her dying son's bedside.[1] I can affirm that neither Madame Surville, nor Monsieur Surville, nor the elder Madame de Balzac came to the house in the Avenue Fortunée that evening. The old woman that Hugo mistook for his mother was a simple nurse . . . and God knows what she was nursing! There was also an old domestic, idle and crafty, the same one that said to Hugo: 'Monsieur is doomed and Madame has gone to her room.' They were almost never in the dying man's room and they were not even there the precise moment that Balzac rendered his last sigh. Neither family, not friends . . .

_____

1 There is absolutely no reason to doubt Victor Hugo's account, but Mirbeau has to dismiss it in order to substitute his own fantasy.

"Gozlan, I remember, was absent from Paris. They neglected to inform Gautier and Laurent-Jan. No publisher was warned, no newspaper. On the day of 18 August 1850, I give you my word of honor, only two people came to Balzac's house: Nacquart, his physician, in the morning, and Hugo, in the evening, at nine o'clock . . . I'm forgetting a third: Madame Victor Hugo asked for Madame de Balzac in the afternoon, and was not admitted . . ."

"And you?" I interrupted.

"Oh, me . . . ," said Jean Gigoux. He shrugged his shoulders, smoothed his long bristling moustache and repeated: "Me! Wait . . . I shall also have my count!"

He went on:

"You know that Balzac had returned from Russia very ill, doomed. He had an arteriosclosis—what they called in those days a hypertrophy of the heart—which he had owed to his crazy work, and something even crazier than his work, the abuse he had made of coffee. Aggravated by chagrin, the malady had progressed rapidly. It was frightful to see. He was suffering like a damned soul, in the chest, the back, the heart. He absolutely could not breathe: asphyxia, there's no other word for it. And he was inflated like a balloon.

Every day he was punctured, but it was soon the case that the punctures no longer relieved him. The trocar screeched, grinding against the flesh of the limbs, which had become hard, impermeable, dry and very red—like salted lard, Doctor Louis said. One can't imagine it! On the seventeenth, during the day, he received the sacraments, along with the three surgeons who were treating him . . ."

Raising his hands toward the ceiling and then letting them fall back on to his thighs heavily, he repeated:

"Who were treating him! Who were treating him! Ah! Finally . . . the three surgeons who were treating him, along with the good Nacquart, withdrew, recommending that they were not to be disturbed again, no matter what might happen! There was nothing further to be done. Balzac was going to die—dying down below, but the top, his head, still remained very much alive. Life was so powerfully anchored in that devil of a man that it could not even decide to quit a body almost entirely decomposed. And throughout the house there was a frightful cadaverous odor. Would you believe that, when I think about that day, that odor comes back to me? That I can't get rid of it? After so many years! But you know all that. That's not what I want to tell you . . ."

He fell silent for a few seconds. Then:

"Listen . . . what I'm going to tell you I haven't yet told to anyone . . . Yes, to Rodin . . . I told it to our friend Rodin, one day when I'd gone to his little house on the Boulevard d'Italie to see a sketch of his *Balzac* . . . Well, promise me that what I'm going to tell you, you won't write, or at least, that you won't write it while I'm alive? Afterwards . . . believe me, whatever you want . . ."

Slightly timid, slightly embarrassed, he added: "Perhaps it's good that people know, one day . . . what happened."

And he went on.

"On the morning of the eighteenth, Nacquart came back. He stayed for more than an hour by his friend's bedside. Balzac was choking. Between his suffocations, however, he was able to ask Nacquart: 'Tell me the truth . . . where am I?'

"Nacquart hesitated. Finally, he replied: 'You have a strong soul . . . I'll tell you the truth. You're doomed.'

"Balzac's face contracted slightly; his fingers scratched at his sheet. He simply said: "Ah!' Then, a little later: 'When am I going to die?'

"With tears in his eyes, the physician replied: 'Perhaps you won't last the night.'

"And they fell silent. In spite of his suffering, Balzac seemed to be reflecting profoundly. Suddenly, he looked at Nacquart, looked at him for a long time, with a kind of resigned smile, in which there was nevertheless a reproach. And he said, in the intervals of his breathlessness: 'Ah! Yes . . . ! I know . . . I need Blanchon . . . I need Blanchon . . . Blanchon will save me!'[1]

"His pride as a creator didn't weaken before death. All his faith in his work he affirmed again in those last words, which he pronounced with a sublime conviction: 'I need Blanchon.' From that moment on the crisis attenuated, gradually relaxing. He seemed to be breathing less dolorously . . .

"Nacquart was fully informed of the dissension in the household. Seeing the patient calmer, perhaps hoping for a softening of his attitude, he asked: 'Have you any instruction to give me? Something to entrust to me? In sum, do you desire anything?'

"To each question, Balzac shook his head and replied: 'No . . . I don't have anything . . . I don't desire anything.'

---

1 Horace Blanchon is a character in *La Comédie humaine*, who treats many of the other characters in numerous volumes in the series.

"Nacquart persisted: 'You don't want to see . . . anyone?'

"'No one.'

"At no time, in the course of that visit, did he mention his wife. It seemed that she no longer existed for him . . . that she had never existed. As Nacquart was about to leave, Balzac asked for paper and a pencil. With a trembling hand he traced a dozen lines . . . but he was so weak that the pencil slipped from his fingers. He said: 'I believe that I'm going to fall asleep. I'll finish this . . . when I feel a little stronger . . .' And he dozed off.

"What had he written? To whom had he written? That piece of paper was never found, which had the same fate as many others, which were not found either . . ."

While he was speaking, Gigoux, who was something of a poseur, like all storytellers, considered me from the corner of his eye, trying to catch my impressions, instead of provoking them. He didn't have the habit of dramatic recitation. His coarse verve, joyful, common and brutal, was ill at ease therein. However, he seemed to me to be sincerely moved. Nevertheless, I listened to him impassively, without interrupting him.

At that moment, he paused and drew breath, passed his hand over his forehead several times, and in a voice that was a little lower, a little less bold, he continued:

"That morning, I had come to see Madame de Balzac early. I found her in a sort of large red peignoir, her arms bare and her hair already done. She hadn't slept during the night. She told me that she hadn't dared go in to the sick man's room . . . that Nacquart was there at the moment . . . that she didn't know what to do . . . that she was very unhappy. 'It's so hard for me,' she moaned. 'I'm afraid to see him.'

"She seemed very overexcited and, at the same time, very depressed. I advised her to show herself, if only for a few minutes, at her husband's bedside. She replied: 'He doesn't even pay attention to my presence. He humiliates me . . . no, no . . . it's too frightful!' And abruptly, in tears: 'You aren't going to leave me alone all day, like yesterday? I nearly went mad . . .'

"Mildly, I reproached her for not wanting to receive anyone, especially Balzac's old friends. I tried to make her see how her attitude would be ill-judged. 'Your disagreements are suspected, but people don't know how profound they are. It's maladroit, I assure you. Do you think that the friends don't talk? That they aren't talking already? Even the domestics . . .'

72

"She became irritated. 'Those people irritate me. I only need you. Oh . . . and yet . . . you too . . . well . . . you irritate me. I no longer love you!'

"It was almost noon when Nacquart, emerging from the dying man's room, asked for her. She only stayed with him for a few minutes and came back into the room very pale, very quickly, and collapsed into an armchair. 'It appears that it's today,' she said, briefly.

"And, her lead tilted forward, her beautiful forehead wrinkled, her eyes vague, she played with the fringes of her red peignoir. 'He's asleep,' she said, then. 'So much the batter if he's no longer suffering.' Suddenly, tapping the arms of the chair: 'Oh, that Nacquart! I detest him . . . I detest him . . .'

"I was horribly embarrassed. Nothing came to my mind but stupid words, banal phrases, readymade, such as one addresses to people who mean nothing to you. How little imagination we have at those moments, or how little sensitivity! Isn't that curious? Making allusion to the bright color of her peignoir, I only found this: 'Truly, my love, you're much too red today.'

"Astonished, she replied, sharply: 'Why? He isn't dead yet.'

73

"She had a meal served that she didn't touch and which, I admit to my shame, I devoured with an appetite. It was execrable, too. We didn't say much. She went from the armchair to the window, came back from the window to the armchair, sometimes filing her fingernails furiously, sometimes uttering sighs. I tried to work out the nature of her emotion. It wasn't grief, not even chagrin, nor remorse, I'm sure of it. It was something like ennui. What preoccupied her most was everything that she would have to do after the death. She never stopped thinking about it and repeating, between long sighs: 'How am I going to get through all that? I don't know, myself . . . ! Such a man . . . so illustrious. There'll be histories and ceremonies. Here . . . I'm totally out of place . . . oh, these days! These days!'

"She was infinitely fearful of Victor Hugo. She had seen him five or six times. His grave politeness, his violent admiration for Balzac, and his profound gaze, which penetrated all the way to the secret soul, frightened her. He would be there, surely. He would speak to her. 'What can I do? No, no . . . I'll never be able to!' And she filed her fingernails more frenziedly.

"In the afternoon we learned from the nurse that Balzac was in his death-throes. Since he had woken up from his doze, he was no longer conscious of things. His eyes were wide open, but he could no longer see anything. He was gasping, with great dull gasps that sometimes lifted his chest as if it were going to burst. More often, he became calm, his head buried in the pillow, without the slightest movement. If it hadn't been for the sound of his throat and the gargling of his nose, one would have thought he was dead. The sheets were soaked by a sudden fetid sweat that was running from his face and his whole body.

"The nurse went on: 'Monsieur has an enormous drop of sweat at the tip of each finger, which the sheet soaks up, and which is renewed incessantly. One would think that he was emptying himself, especially through the fingers . . . it's extraordinary.' She had never seen that before. She said: 'Oh, Madame had better not go in. Truly, it isn't engaging, for a lady. I've watched a lot, as you can imagine! But ones like Monsieur . . . oh la la! And I've used a lot of chlorine . . .' And she also said: 'I'll need a pair of nice sheets soon, for when I do the dressing . . . the valet de chambre only has old ones . . .'

"And as the poor woman, frightened by all those details, repeated 'The dressing! My God! There's that! The dressing . . .' The nurse reassured her with a frightful smile: 'Oh, Madame has no need to be there . . . Madame shouldn't torment herself. It's nothing. I'm used to it!'

"The day passed thus, lugubrious and slow, eternal. I wasn't permitted to leave, to attend to my affairs, to go to my studio, where I had an important meeting. Every time I expressed the desire, she clung on to me, uttering little cries. 'No, no . . . don't leave me on my own here. Your studio! Stay with me, I beg you!' If the nurse presented herself in order to ask for something she was lacking, or to bring us up to date with the progress of the death-throes, she blocked her ears, not wanting to hear anything. She even begged her only to come back when 'everything is finished.'

"The sort of belated child, bewildered animal, that a woman like Madame de Balzac can become, who had the reputation—exaggerated of course—of being a superior, energetic, brilliant creature . . . I would never have believed it possible, to that point. For I've always seen, on the contrary, women stronger than events, giving men the example of courage, endurance and self-control. She . . . she was no longer anything . . . no longer anything. She was no longer a rational being, not even a madwoman, not even a beast . . . Oh, what a pity! She was nothing. Vanquished by fatigue, numbed by the heat of that sealed room, she consented to lie down on the chaise longue, where she slept, a painful, troubled slumber, until nightfall.

"I had picked up a book . . . *Le Médecin de campagne*, as I remember . . . an unstitched, torn copy, dirty by virtue of having been read and re-read. But what can I tell you? I was utterly brutalized, as incapable of reading anything as I was of thinking anything at all. I only experienced one sensation . . . the ennui of not knowing what to do . . . of not knowing what to say . . . the ennui of being there. Above all, I was suffering cruelly from not being able to smoke. And in that house in the middle of Paris, where, more neglected than a beast dying at the bottom of a hole in the woods, the greatest genius of the century was dying, I listened, without being impressed by the atrocity of the drama. I listened to the immense, lugubrious silence that was only troubled, from time to time, by the human sound, the unique human sound, of two filthy slippers trudging along the corridor on the other side of the door."

Gigoux stopped. He seemed fatigued. Perhaps he hesitated to say any more. That old man, whom I had always known so skeptical in life, so devoid of prejudices, except in his art, who made cynicism a sort of intellectual adornment and a moral law of existence, was, before me, timid and uncertain, like a child caught at fault. Now he turned his head away, in order not to meet my gaze. I thought that he didn't dare, couldn't say any more . . . I was willing him to make the dolorous effort that, visibly, he would have to make in order to continue and finish his story . . .

Finally, he made the decision.

"At half-past ten, exactly, someone struck two violent blows of the bedroom door. 'Madame! Madame!' I recognized the shrill, yapping voice of the nurse. 'Madame! Madame!' the voice repeated. And a few seconds later: 'Come, Madame, come! Monsieur is passing!' Then two more blows, so rudely struck that I thought the lock had broken and that the nurse had come into the room . . .

"We were sitting up in bed. And, necks craned, mouths open, motionless, we looked at one another, without a word . . .

"Swiftly, she had slid one leg out of the sheets, as if to get up. 'Wait!' I said, holding her by the wrists.

"Why *wait*? Wait for what? I had murmured that in a low voice, mechanically stupidly, without it corresponding to any idea, any intention on my part. I could just as well have said; 'Hurry!' But the voice had fallen silent. There was no longer anyone behind the door. And already, I could hear the two slippers drawing away in the corridor, clicking . . . then a door, further away, opening . . . a door closing . . . then silence.

"Her loose hair was covering her face like a crepe veil, falling in black waves over her shoulders, from which the nightdress had slid. She finally whispered: 'It's stupid! It's stupid! I should have responded . . . what will she think? No, truly, it's too stupid!' But she still didn't budge, her leg still hanging out of the sheets. And she repeated, in a scarcely perceptible voice: 'It's stupid! Why have you stopped me, held me back?'

"And obstinately, I said: 'Wait. She'll come back.'

"'No, no, she knows you're here. I should have responded. And now . . .'

"'She'll come back. Wait.'

"In fact, after ten minutes, which seemed to us to be hours and hours, the nurse came back. Two knocks on the door, like the first time, and: 'Madame! Madame!' Then: 'Monsieur has passed. Monsieur is dead . . .'"

At this point, the old painter interrupted himself, and shook his head.

"Let me," he said, "confess something unusual to you . . . something inexplicable. It isn't to excuse myself . . . to defend myself . . . it's . . . Anyway, here goes! I assure you that that 'Monsieur is dead,' didn't evoke anything in me at first, nothing precise . . . above all, nothing formidable. I didn't associate the idea of Balzac with it. I didn't see, suddenly looming up, the colossal figure of Balzac, eyes closed, mouth closed, chilled forever . . . no . . . I was so outside myself, outside all consciousness, all verity . . . I was drowned in such moral darkness that the news, cried behind that door, with which the entire world was going to resound the next day, didn't impress me any more than if I had learned it about any man . . . that an unknown man was dead. I didn't say to myself: 'Balzac is dead.' Instead, I asked myself: 'Who's dead?' In fact, I didn't ask myself anything at all. By virtue of an exceptional phenomenon of amnesia, I really forgot that I was, at the very moment when he died . . . in Balzac's house, in Balzac's bed, with Balzac's wife! Can you understand that?"

He smiled bitterly, an almost comical gesture, which expressed the astonishment of "not having understood that," and he went on.

"At the cry of 'Monsieur is dead,' she had got up with a bound and started running around the room, barefoot, without knowing what she was doing either, or where she was. 'My God! My God!' she moaned. 'It's your fault! It's your fault!' She went from one armchair to another, one item of furniture to another, picking up and throwing down my scattered clothes and hers, which had fallen on the carpet. She knocked over a chair, bumped into a table, from which the dessert hadn't been removed after dinner. And the mirrors multiplied her maddened image, more naked by the second . . .

"The blows redoubled, more deafening, the voice called out, more high-pitched: 'Madame! Madame! Hey, Madame!'

"I saw that she was about to go out, completely nude. 'Where are you going?' I cried. 'At least put some clothes on. And then calm down!'

"I got up, obliged her to put her stockings on, to put on a sort of white peignoir, very dirty, that I had found in the dressing room. As she tried to go out again: 'What about your hair? Come on . . . arrange your hair.'

"She was sobbing, lamenting. 'Oh, why did I go with him? I didn't want to . . . I didn't want to . . . it was him . . . you know what he's like . . . and you . . . why did you come, today? It's your fault. And that old woman? What is she going to think . . . ? My God! My God! And my daughter . . . ? My poor child . . . ! It's horrible! I'll never be able . . .'

"Meanwhile, she collected her hair, twisted it, fastened it over the nape in a large bundle, from which long wisps escaped. 'No, no . . . I don't want to go there . . . I don't want to see him. Take me back to Russia . . . right away . . . right away . . . take me, say you will?'

"And, as further blows were hammered on the door, in response to further appeals, almost insulting, her peignoir poorly fastened, her head all tousled, without slippers on her feet, she ran out, shouting: 'Yes, yes . . . it's me . . . I'm coming . . . I'm coming . . .'

"I went back to bed. Lying on the covers, legs bare, chest in the air, arms tucked behind my neck, without thinking about anything . . . without any emotion of what had just happened, without any terror of the proximity of that dead man, for a long time, I considered my toes, to which I imparted the disorderly movements and gestures of marionettes.

"The silence of the house had something so heavy, so uninhabited about it that it didn't seem real. With that, odors of amour arrived at my nostrils, and also sickening odors of food and drink, sharpened by the heat. My clothes, and her skirts, were draped over the furniture and strewn on the carpet, in such disorder and so undignified that, if it hadn't been for the regal splendor of the bed and the shiny bronze fitments of the looking-glass, I could have believed that I'd run aground after drinking, at the hazard of some nocturnal encounter, in the home of some prostitute. To complete the illusion, to my left, through the open door of the cabinet, I perceived a kettle warming over a little lamp . . .

"I stayed there like that for five hours, during which, to prove to me that everything wasn't dead in the house, I tried to perceive, here and there, while half-asleep, the sound of whispers and comings and goings along the corridor. It wasn't cheerful, certainly, but nor was it very painful either . . . Deep down, I wasn't sorry to be free, I was almost enjoying being alone.

"When Madame de Balzac returned, I had let a little air into the room and had got dressed. She was extremely pale and distraught. Her swollen eyelids, very red, showed that she must have wept a great deal. 'It's finished,' she said. 'He's dead . . . he's really dead.' She let herself fall on to the edge of the bed, covered her face with her hands and sighed: 'It's frightful!' And, shaken by a long frisson, she repeated: 'It's frightful . . . it's frightful that he smells bad!'

"She didn't give me any details. To all my questions she only replied with moans . . . brief, irritated moans. She had a bitter, almost malevolent crease at the corner of her mouth. And the mouth, so prettily sensual in its design, then took on a vulgar, base expression in which there was something repulsive. I asked her whether she had informed the family. 'Tomorrow . . . tomorrow . . .' she said. 'What do you expect, at this hour?' Her voice, completely changed, without the singing tone that I liked so much in her, became aggressive.

"As she looked at me, as she looked at the bed and the disorder in the room, she had a sort of retch. I thought that she was about to burst into tears, or a fit of fury. I helped her to lie down on the bed. 'You'll have a very tiring day tomorrow . . . a great many people . . . lots to do. Rest. Try to sleep . . .'

"'Yes, yes,' she said, 'I'm exhausted.'

"It was four o'clock in the morning. Dawn was about to break.

"Gently, tenderly, I said to her 'You mustn't hold it against me for leaving you. Be good . . . it's necessary. It wouldn't be appropriate for me to be seen in your house at such a time.'

84

"I expected a scene, tears. She didn't protest, and didn't try to retain me. 'Yes, you're right,' she said, in a dry one. 'It's better thus. Go away!' And, as I didn't leave immediately, looking for something in the room, she repeated, in a harsher tone: 'Go away! Well then, get out!' She turned to the wall, with an affectation that astonished me.

"She refused my kiss. 'It's all right . . . it's all right . . . leave me, I beg you . . .' Was it fatigue? Was it disgust? Or what? I said: '*À bientôt*, then.'

"'As you wish,' she said.

"I went out. There was no one in the corridor, no sound in the house. A lamp was about to go out on a small table. Its tremulous light made huge shadows move over the walls. As I went past Balzac's room I almost bumped into a chair on which the nurse had piled bundles of soiled linen, which gave off an abominable odor of putrescence. I stopped, however. I listened. Nothing . . . the creak of an item of furniture, that was all! I had a tremor in the heart and a sort of strangulation in the throat. For a moment, I thought about going in; I didn't dare. I also thought about fetching my box of colors and making a rapid sketch of the great man on his deathbed. That idea seemed impossible and mad. 'No, no, not me!' I said to myself. 'That would be too dirty a trick.'

"Then I went downstairs slowly, on tiptoe. At the bottom there was the kitchen. The door was ajar and it was illuminated. The sound of voices was coming from it, those of the nurse and the valet de chambre. They were cheerfully having supper, I swear! By moving closer I could have heard what they were saying, but I didn't dare do that either, for fear that they were talking about me . . . about us. The other servants had doubtless gone to their rooms and were asleep. Up there, Balzac was alone, all alone!

"Once in the street, I uttered a long sigh of relief; I breathed in the fresh morning air with delight, and I lit a cigar."

Suddenly getting to his feet, Jean Gigoux marched around the studio, with his hands behind his back . . . marched around the studio for a long time. And, stopping in front of me, he said: "And that's how Balzac died. Balzac! Do you hear? Balzac! That's how he died!"

Then he resumed marching. After a brief silence, he said: "It's funny. I'm not a wicked man, though . . . I'm not a wretch . . . a swine . . . My God! I'm like everyone else. Well, I truly didn't understand until later . . . much later. Certainly, that day . . . that night . . . I was embarrassed . . . stupid . . . I don't know . . . disgusted. I sensed that it wasn't right . . . yes, but what was it? What? Ignominy? No, I give you my word of honor . . . it wasn't until later . . . What do you expect? One loves a woman . . . one lets oneself go . . . and it's always, always, dirtiness! Ah! And then, did I really love her?"

He opened his arms, and then brought them back swiftly to his body, making his hands slap against his thighs.

"In truth . . . I don't know any longer." Shrugging his shoulders, he added: "Man is a dirty pig . . . that's all I know . . . a dirty pig!"

He made several tours of the studio, tapping the furniture, displacing the chairs, mumbling: "Balzac! Balzac! A Balzac!"

Then he came to sit down again, abruptly, in the armchair, facing me.

"As for Madame de Balzac . . ." He stressed every word, with a heavy irony that shocked me slightly. "As for Madame de Balzac," he repeated, "the next day, she had pulled herself together. Oh, completely! She was very dignified, very noble, very grief-stricken, very literary. Marvelous, my dear. Andromache herself, when she lost Hector. She amazed and touched everyone with her tragic correctness, the beauty of her attitude. What a line! What a line for a Prix de Rome! People surrounded her, people felt sorry for her . . . what do you think? The most comical thing is that I truly believe that she was sincere in her play-acting. The consideration, the respect and the tributes restored her grief and her amour. I couldn't get over it, myself, although I'd got over many things before! Oh, that funeral . . . !"

His smile was almost cheerful.

"My dear . . . can you imagine . . . the minister Baroche, who was representing the government, walking in the procession next to Victor Hugo, said to him: 'Fundamentally, Monsieur de Balzac was—wasn't he?—a rather distinguished man?'

Hugo looked at that minister—who has such a fine press in *Les Châtiments*—he looked at him, bewildered and scandalized, and replied: 'He was a genius, Monsieur, the greatest genius of the era,' And he turned his back on him. Hugo has recounted that somewhere . . . nothing is more true. I happened to be beside him when that little scene occurred. But what Hugo perhaps never knew is that the minister Baroche, addressing his other neighbor, who had, I recall, very fine side-whiskers, said to him in a whisper: 'That Monsieur Hugo is much crazier than people think . . .'"

And Gigoux started to laugh frankly, one of those sonorous bursts of laughter that he had, even when he was very old. He added: "So, later, he got his promotion . . . he hadn't stolen it, eh?"[1]

Then he said: "Oh, do you know this detail? When, the day after his death, the molders came to make a mold of Balzac's face, they were obliged to go away empty-handed, my dear. The decomposition had been so rapid that the flesh of the face had been completely corroded. The entire nose had flowed over the sheet."

---

1 Jules Baroche (1802-1870), the Minister of the Interior in the Republican government when Balzac died, went on to have a long career during the Second Empire, in spite of refusing to lend his support to the *coup d'état*. He was the Minister of Justice and Public Worship from 1863-69. Not unnaturally, the exiled Victor Hugo disapproved of him strongly, and made his feelings clear in *Les Châtiments* (1853).

A PARTIAL LIST OF SNUGGLY BOOKS

Printed in the USA
CPSIA information can be obtained
at www.ICGtesting.com
CBHW021344040424
6379CB00012B/1043